ON
PHONICS

Learn to read with
Dog in the Fog

Words by Sue Graves
Illustrations by Jan Smith

book-studio

"You must get in shape, Pog," said Mr. Mog to his dog.

"I think," said Pog, "I'll go out for a jog."

"Oh no!"
said Pog.
"I can't see
in this fog."

"Oops!" said Pog as he tripped over a log.

"Ouch!" said Pog as he bumped into a hog.

"Look where you are going!"

"I'm going home. I don't like this fog," said Pog.

"Pooh! What a wet, smelly dog." said Mr. Mog.

The end